P9-BYZ-609

Snow Tracks

by Liza Charlesworth

ISBN-13: 978-0-545-25773-2 / ISBN-10: 0-545-25773-5

Illustrated by Anne Kennedy
Designed by Maria Lilja • Colored by Ka-yeon Kim-Li
Copyright © 2010 by Liza Charlesworth

SCHOLASTIC

Who left these tracks in the snow?

It was a horse on the go!

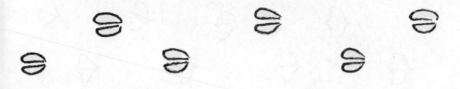

Who left these tracks in the snow?

It was a deer on the go!

3

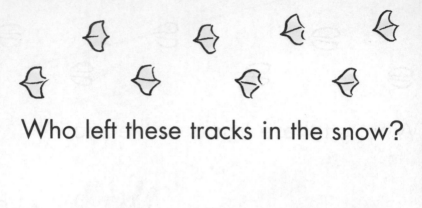

Who left these tracks in the snow?

It was a duck on the go!

Who left these tracks in the snow?

It was a fox on the go!

Who left these tracks in the snow?

It was a dog on the go!

Who left these tracks in the snow?

It was a rabbit on the go!

Who left these tracks in the snow?

It was a kid on the go!